Places of the World

Neil Morris

Introduction

There are wonderful places to see and visit on all of the world's continents – North America, South America, Europe, Africa, Asia and Australasia. The seventh continent, Antarctica, is very cold and covered in ice and snow.

Many of the places that make up the stickers in this book are natural wonders of the world. There are long rivers, huge dry deserts, wet marshes, beautiful lakes, big mountain ranges with tall peaks, as well as fascinating underground caves and plunging waterfalls. Many of them are the biggest, longest or highest of their kind, which makes them very special. Others have particular meaning for local people, such as Uluru to the Aborigines of Australia or the River Ganges to the Hindus of India.

Other places are man-made wonders of the world. Down the centuries people have created wonderful buildings, magnificent monuments and many other structures that are triumphs of design and engineering. It would be difficult to visit them all on six different continents, but at least we can do so in this book!

Fact file 1

On top of the world

The Himalayas form the world's highest mountain range. They stretch across the border between India and Tibet, through the small kingdoms of Bhutan and Nepal to northern Pakistan. The ten highest mountains in the world are all in the Himalayas, which in the ancient Indian language of Sanskrit means "home of snow". At the western end of the mountain system are the Karakoram Mountains and the Hindu Kush. The Himalayan mountain peaks are always covered in snow, and every year they get a tiny bit higher as the mountains are pushed upwards.

Did you know?

The tallest Himalayan peak, Mount Everest, is the highest mountain in the world. Recent mountain surveys have measured Everest at 8863 metres. The mountain was named after a British Surveyor General, George Everest. To the people of Tibet it is known as Qomolongma, or "goddess mother of the world". Mountaineers first tried to climb Everest in 1920, but it took until 1953 for climbers to reach the very top.

Longest mountain range

The Andes is the longest mountain range in the world. The Andes mountains stretch all the way down South America and form part of seven countries – Venezuela, Colombia, Ecuador, Peru, Bolivia, Argentina and Chile. This makes a total length of 7200 kilometres, almost twice as long as the Himalayas. La Paz, in Bolivia, is the highest capital city in the world. It lies 3631 metres high in the Andes, and more than a million people live there. Before the Spanish conquest of South America, the Incas and other Native American peoples were the main inhabitants of the Andes.

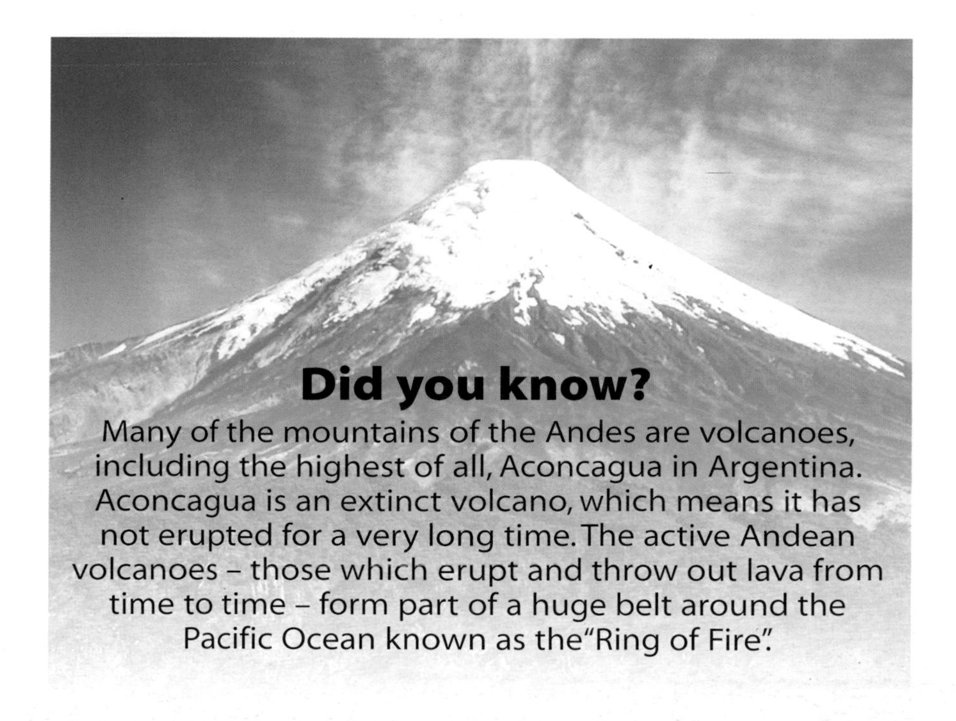

Did you know?

Many of the mountains of the Andes are volcanoes, including the highest of all, Aconcagua in Argentina. Aconcagua is an extinct volcano, which means it has not erupted for a very long time. The active Andean volcanoes – those which erupt and throw out lava from time to time – form part of a huge belt around the Pacific Ocean known as the "Ring of Fire".

The Americas

The world's two longest mountain ranges are in the Americas. The Rockies stretch down the continent of North America, and the Andes run all the way down South America. There are many forests, deserts and waterfalls, as well as cities and pyramids built by ancient Native American peoples. But this is also a very modern part of the world. The world's biggest tower stands in Canada, and space shuttles blast off from Florida.

CN TOWER

The world's tallest free-standing structure towers over Toronto, Canada.

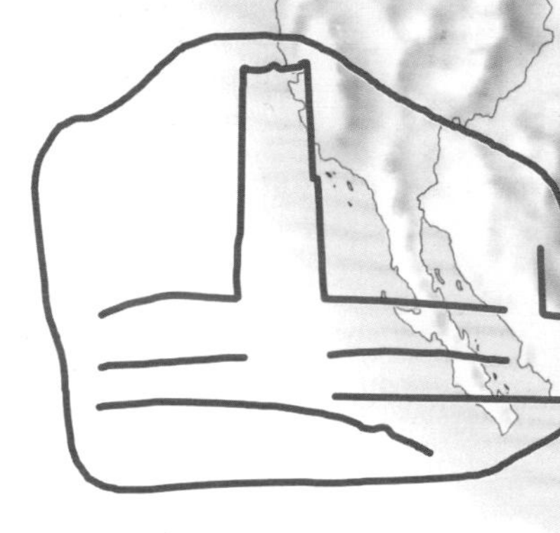

GOLDEN GATE BRIDGE

This suspension bridge in San Francisco, USA, is 1280 m long.

CANADIAN PACIFIC RAILROAD

Canada's transcontinental railway was completed in 1885.

GRAND CANYON

The world's biggest canyon, in Arizona, USA, is 1600 m deep.

MOUNT RUSHMORE

A gigantic sculpture of four US presidents in South Dakota.

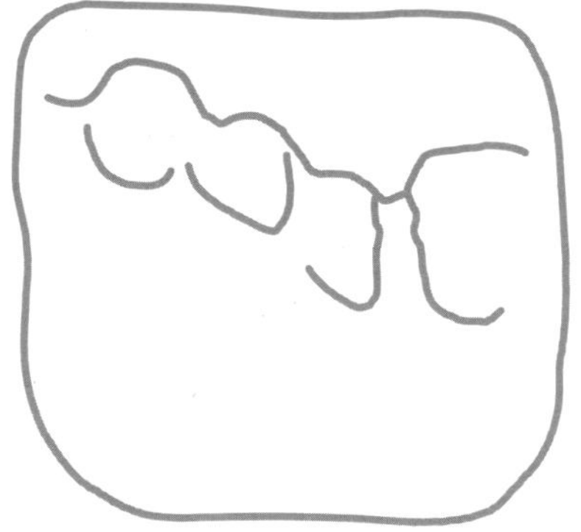

EVERGLADES

This huge swamp in Florida, USA, is now a national park.

MAYAN PYRAMID

The Maya people of Mexico and Central America built huge pyramid temples.

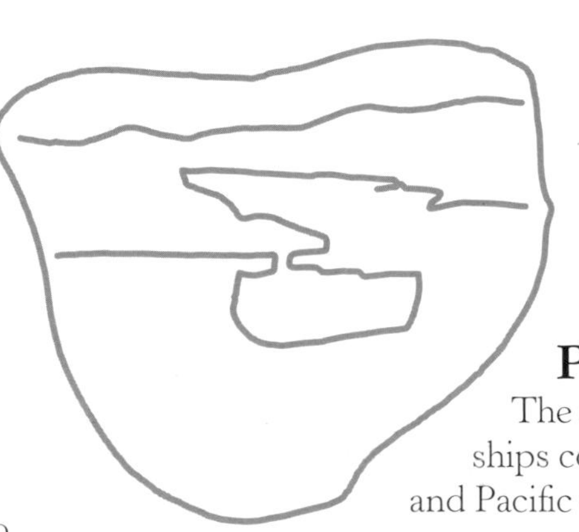

EASTER ISLAND

Mysterious ancient stone figures stand on this Pacific island.

PANAMA CANAL

The canal opened in 1914 so that ships could sail between the Atlantic and Pacific oceans.

OLMEC HEAD

The ancient Olmecs of Mexico carved giant stone heads.

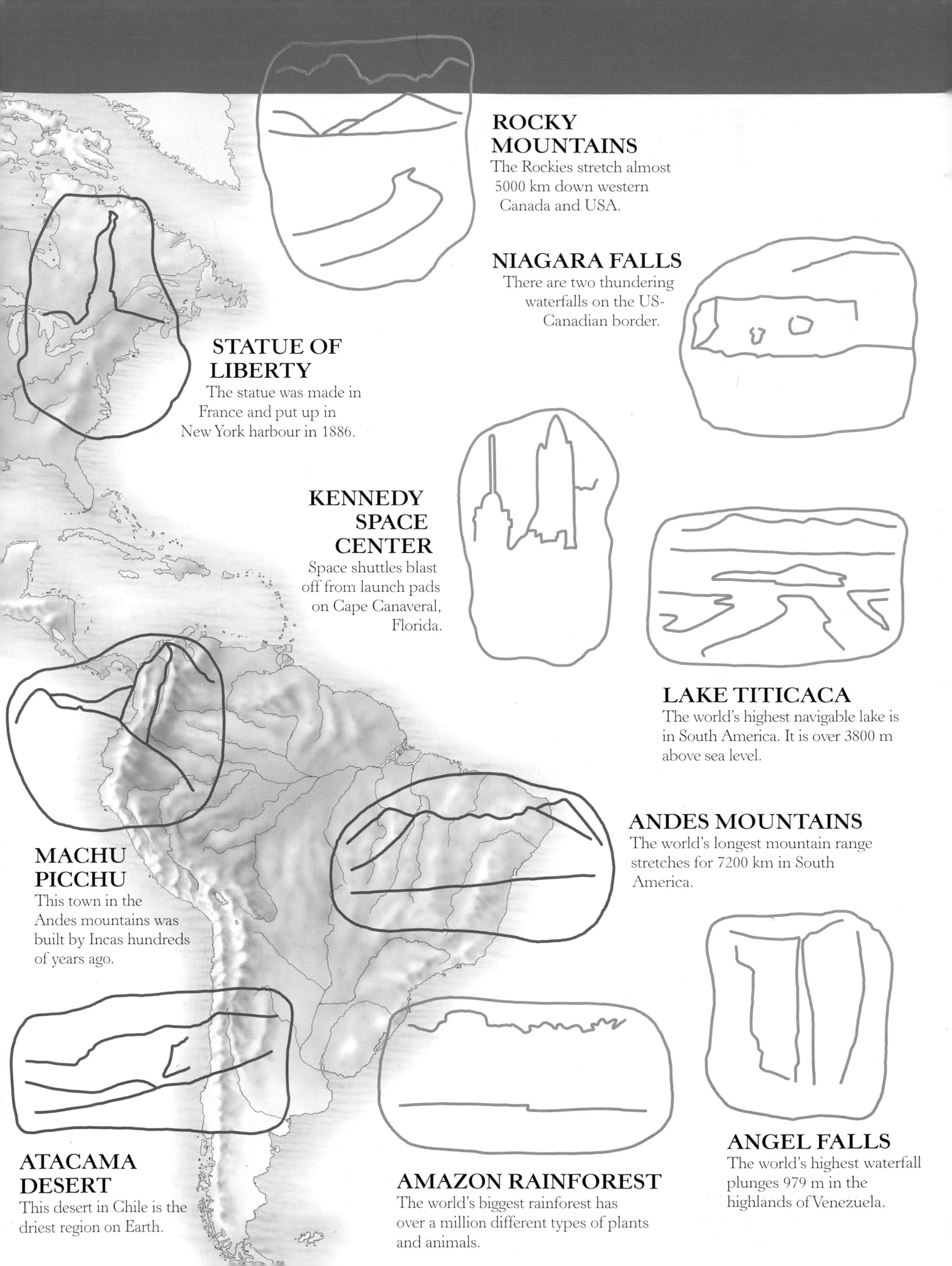
ROCKY MOUNTAINS
The Rockies stretch almost 5000 km down western Canada and USA.
NIAGARA FALLS
There are two thundering waterfalls on the US-Canadian border.
STATUE OF LIBERTY
The statue was made in France and put up in New York harbour in 1886.
KENNEDY SPACE CENTER
Space shuttles blast off from launch pads on Cape Canaveral, Florida.
LAKE TITICACA
The world's highest navigable lake is in South America. It is over 3800 m above sea level.
MACHU PICCHU
This town in the Andes mountains was built by Incas hundreds of years ago.
ANDES MOUNTAINS
The world's longest mountain range stretches for 7200 km in South America.
ATACAMA DESERT
This desert in Chile is the driest region on Earth.
AMAZON RAINFOREST
The world's biggest rainforest has over a million different types of plants and animals.
ANGEL FALLS
The world's highest waterfall plunges 979 m in the highlands of Venezuela.

Fact file 2

Castle of the knights

The great fortress of Krak des Chevaliers (French-Arabic for "castle of the knights"), in Syria, is one of the finest in the world. It was built by Christian crusaders, who fought to recapture the Holy Land from the Muslims. The castle was built on a former Muslim stronghold in 1142. It had two high walls, 13 towers and was practically impossible to attack. It held a garrison of 2000 soldiers with their horses, fighting equipment and enough food to last for five years.

Did you know?

During the Middle Ages in Europe, a lord's castle was both a home and a fortified stronghold. The lord lived with his family and loyal followers in the central tower. This was surrounded by a high wall, often with a water-filled moat around it. A drawbridge over the moat led to the main entrance. If the castle was threatened, the drawbridge was raised, and the opening in the wall was sealed off by a portcullis, a heavy gate lowered from above.

In the Valley of the Kings

Many of the later pharaohs, or kings, of ancient Egypt were buried in royal tombs in the Valley of the Kings. This canyon is on the west bank of the River Nile near the ancient city of Thebes. In 1922 the archaeologist Howard Carter discovered the tomb of Tutankhamun there. It was full of golden objects, including a gold mask which covered the head and shoulders of the royal mummy. Tutankhamun had died over 3000 years earlier, at the age of about 18.

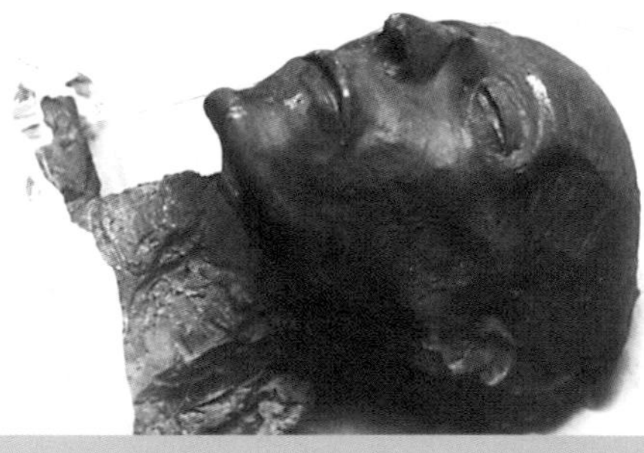

Did you know?

The ancient Egyptians believed that they needed their bodies for a new life after death. So important people, such as pharaohs, had their bodies preserved as mummies. First, surgeons removed the body's internal organs. Then the body was treated with salt and oils, and wrapped in bandages before being placed in a coffin. Tutankhamun's body was mummified.

The Americas

Amazon rainforest

Easter Island

Lake Titicaca

Andes Mountains

Mayan pyramid

Angel Falls

Panama Canal

Machu Picchu

Olmec head

Atacama Desert

The Americas

Rocky Mountains

Niagara Falls

Mount Rushmore

Golden Gate Bridge

CN Tower

Grand Canyon

Canadian Pacific Railroad

Statue of Liberty

Kennedy Space Center

Everglades

Europe and Africa

Alhambra

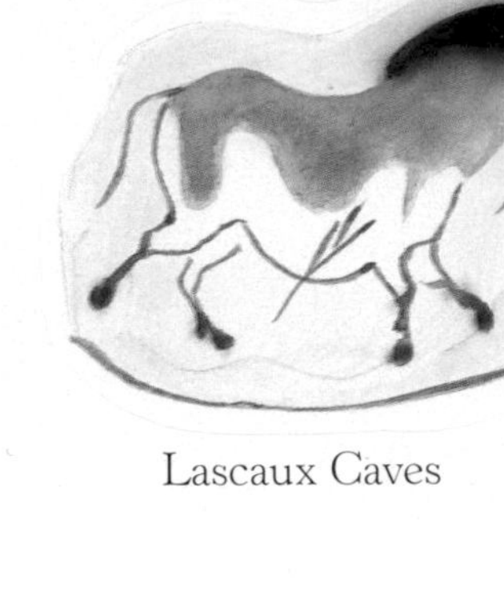

Lascaux Caves

Loire chateau

Stave church

Stonehenge

Big Ben

Parthenon

Colosseum

Eiffel Tower

Neuschwanstein

Europe and Africa

Pyramids

Sahara Desert

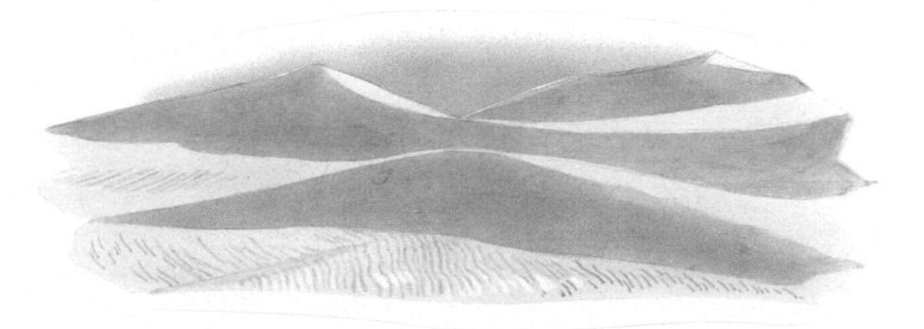

Skeleton Coast

Suez Canal

Victoria Falls

River Nile

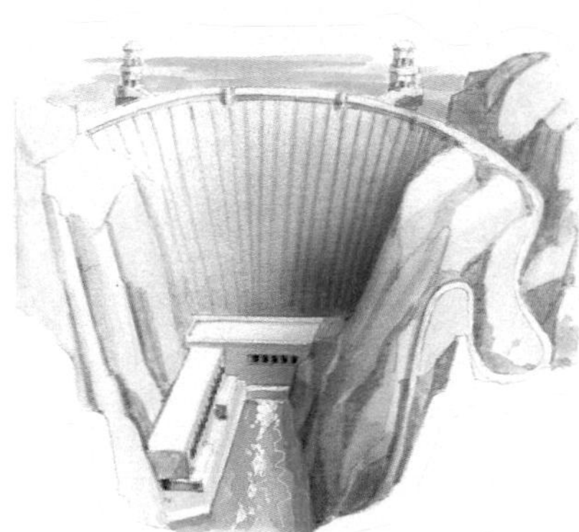

Aswan High Dam

Mount Kilimanjaro

Great Zimbabwe

Oasis

Asia and Australasia

River Ganges

Taj Mahal

Mount Fuji

Petra

Sundarbans

St Basil's Cathedral

Kuwait

Golden Temple

Angkor Wat

Great Wall of China

Asia and Australasia

Blue Mountains

Uluru

Lake Eyre

Rotorua Springs

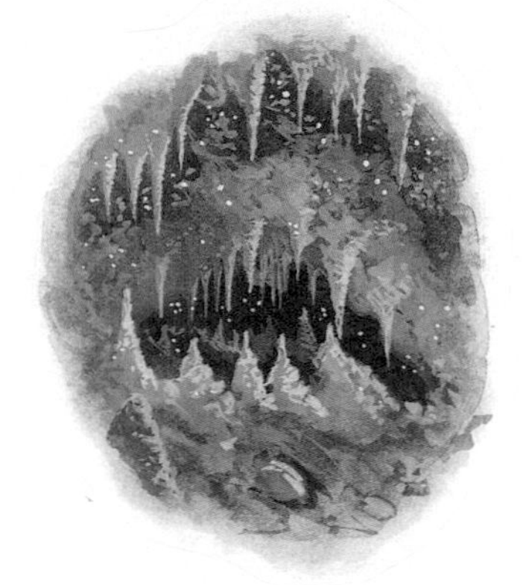

Waitomo Cave

Aboriginal paintings

Wave Rock

Sydney Opera House

Maori meeting house

Great Barrier Reef

Vital statistics

Did you know?

Most of the world's large deserts are very hot places. The largest desert of all, the Sahara in northern Africa, reaches temperatures up to 50°C. In hot deserts the temperature often falls very low at night, sometimes by as much as 25°C. But not all deserts are hot. The Gobi Desert, in central Asia, gets very cold indeed in winter.

World's biggest deserts

1	Sahara	8 400 000 square kilometres
2	Australian	1 550 000 sq km
3	Arabian	1 300 000 sq km
4	Gobi	1 040 000 sq km
5	Kalahari	520 000 sq km
6	Takla Makan	320 000 sq km
7	Sonoran	310 000 sq km
8	Namib	300 000 sq km
9	Kara Kum	270 000 sq km
10	Thar	260 000 sq km

World's longest rivers

1	Nile	6670 km
2	Amazon	6448 km
3	Chang Jiang	6300 km
4	Mississippi	6020 km
5	Yenisei	5540 km
6	Huang He	5464 km
7	Ob	5409 km
8	Parana	4880 km
9	Congo	4700 km
10	Lena	4400 km

Did you know?

Long rivers have many smaller branches, or tributaries. Each tributary has a different source and may have a different name. To find the length of a river, we measure from the source that is furthest from the river's mouth. The Nile begins as the River Kagera in the central African country of Burundi, and flows all the way through Sudan and Egypt to its mouth at the Mediterranean Sea.

Europe and Africa

With its long history of different cultures, Europe has many places that teach us about the past. But some still remain mysteries. What did people use the stones of Stonehenge for, and why did prehistoric people paint in the caves of Lascaux? Africa has similar fascinating places, such as Great Zimbabwe and the famous Pyramids. The world's largest desert is there too, and the longest river runs along its edge.

STONEHENGE
Circles of huge stones have stood for thousands of years on Salisbury Plain in England.

LASCAUX CAVES
Prehistoric paintings were found on the walls of these French caves in 1940.

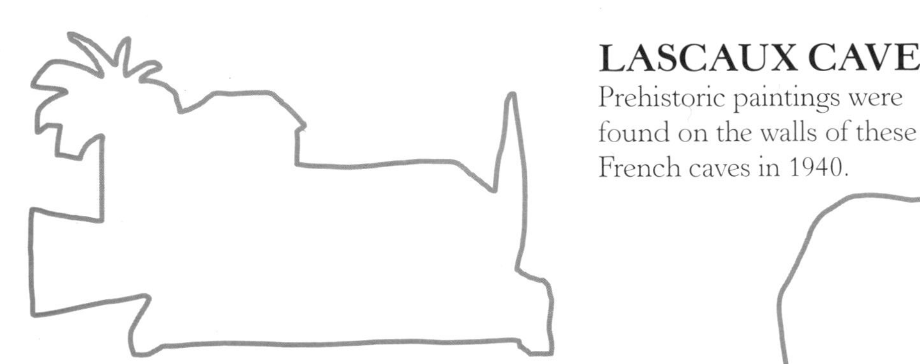

ALHAMBRA
This Spanish citadel was built by the Moors when they ruled Spain.

SAHARA DESERT
The world's largest desert covers most of northern Africa.

LOIRE CHATEAU
This beautiful French castle is like a fortified country house.

RIVER NILE
The world's longest river flows from central Africa to the Mediterranean Sea.

EIFFEL TOWER
The famous landmark of Paris was built for a great exhibition in 1889.

COLOSSEUM
This ancient Roman amphitheatre held 50,000 people 2000 years ago.

SKELETON COAST
This part of the Namib Desert got its name from its many shipwrecks.

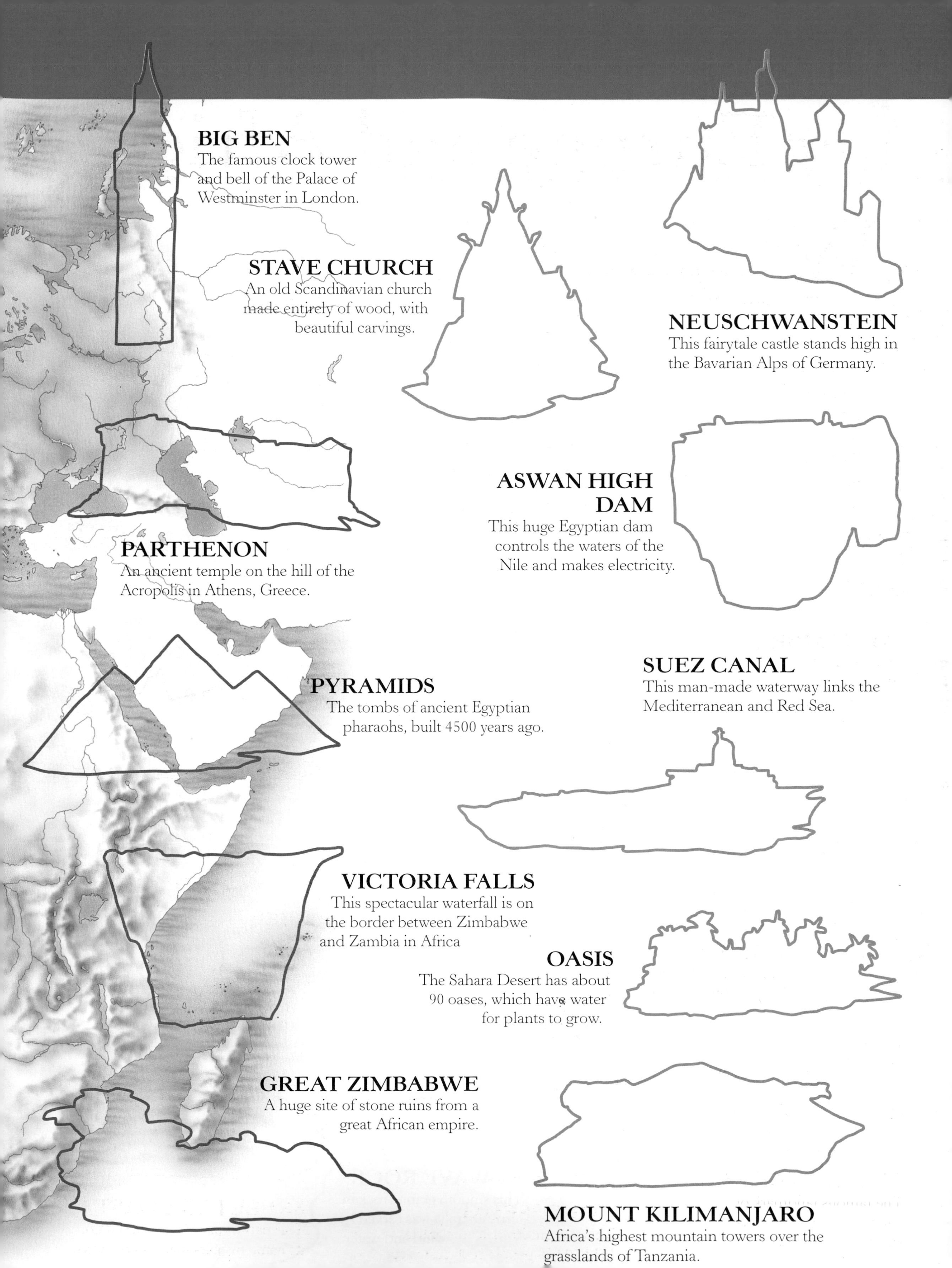
BIG BEN
The famous clock tower and bell of the Palace of Westminster in London.
STAVE CHURCH
An old Scandinavian church made entirely of wood, with beautiful carvings.
NEUSCHWANSTEIN
This fairytale castle stands high in the Bavarian Alps of Germany.
PARTHENON
An ancient temple on the hill of the Acropolis in Athens, Greece.
ASWAN HIGH DAM
This huge Egyptian dam controls the waters of the Nile and makes electricity.
PYRAMIDS
The tombs of ancient Egyptian pharaohs, built 4500 years ago.
SUEZ CANAL
This man-made waterway links the Mediterranean and Red Sea.
VICTORIA FALLS
This spectacular waterfall is on the border between Zimbabwe and Zambia in Africa
OASIS
The Sahara Desert has about 90 oases, which have water for plants to grow.
GREAT ZIMBABWE
A huge site of stone ruins from a great African empire.
MOUNT KILIMANJARO
Africa's highest mountain towers over the grasslands of Tanzania.

Asia and Australasia

The continent of Asia has had a varied and colourful history and is full of ancient buildings and temples. The world's largest country, Russia, lies mostly in Asia, although the western end of this vast land spreads into neighbouring Europe. Australasia has a rich heritage of Aborigine, Maori and Pacific island culture. There are many wonders to be seen here, including the world's biggest coral reef.

PETRA
This ancient town in Jordan was once a great trading centre.

GOLDEN TEMPLE
This temple, at Amritsar in India, is the centre of the Sikh religion.

TAJ MAHAL
This beautiful marble building in India was built as a tomb for a ruler's wife.

KUWAIT
Kuwait City is the modern capital of a small country rich in oil.

RIVER GANGES
This river in northern India is sacred to all Hindus.

LAKE EYRE
This huge salt lake in Australia only holds water after very heavy rains.

SUNDARBANS
This huge swamp in Bangladesh teems with snakes and crocodiles.

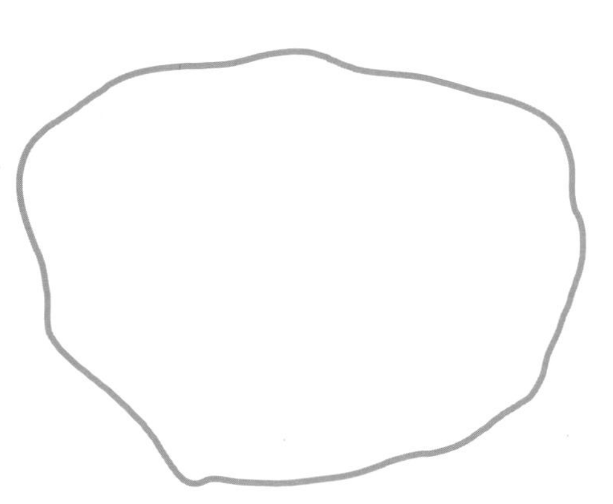

BLUE MOUNTAINS
The mountains are covered in eucalyptus trees, which give off a fine blue mist.

WAVE ROCK
This smooth granite rock in Western Australia was carved by wind and water.

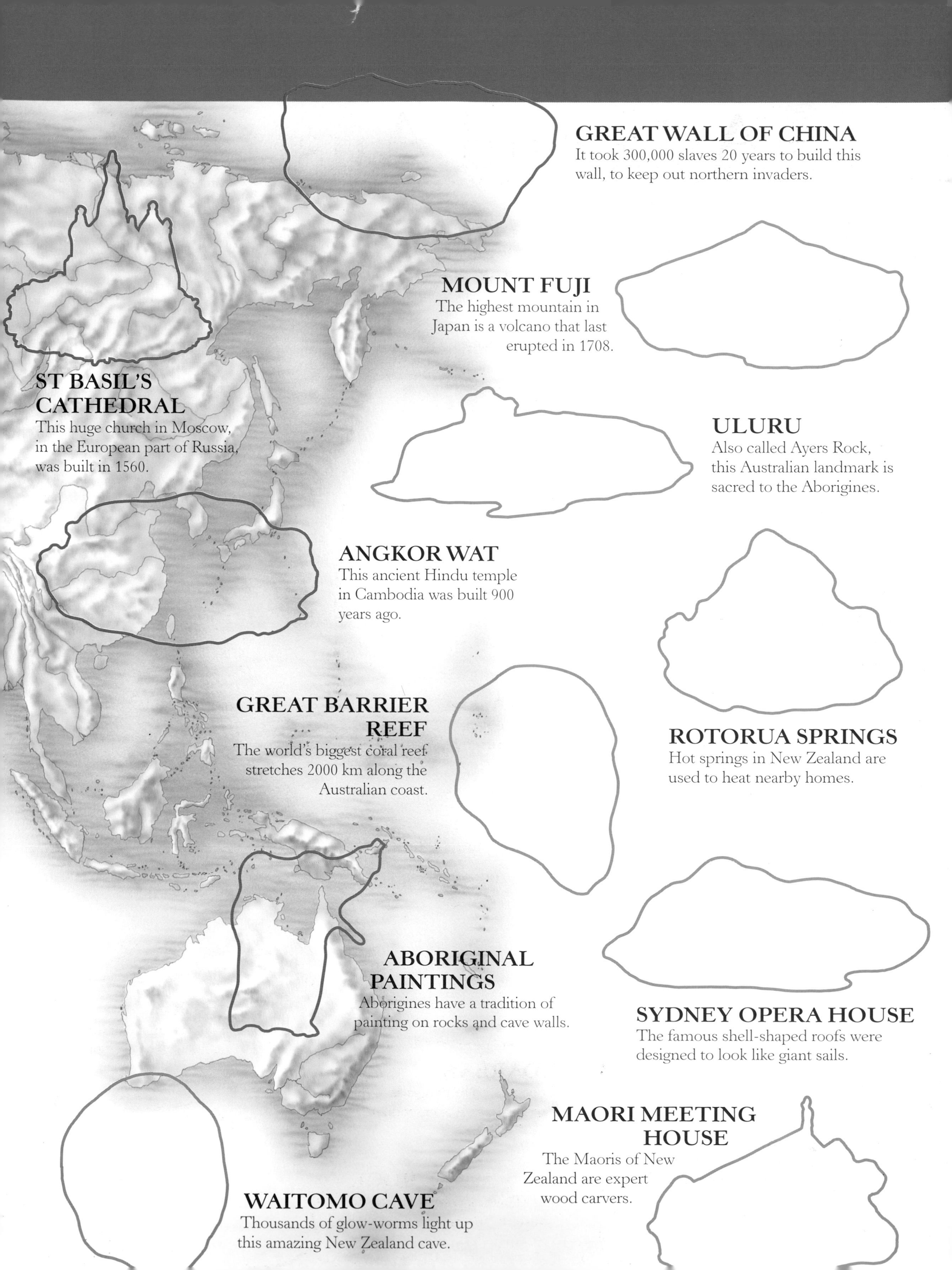

GREAT WALL OF CHINA
It took 300,000 slaves 20 years to build this wall, to keep out northern invaders.

MOUNT FUJI
The highest mountain in Japan is a volcano that last erupted in 1708.

ST BASIL'S CATHEDRAL
This huge church in Moscow, in the European part of Russia, was built in 1560.

ULURU
Also called Ayers Rock, this Australian landmark is sacred to the Aborigines.

ANGKOR WAT
This ancient Hindu temple in Cambodia was built 900 years ago.

GREAT BARRIER REEF
The world's biggest coral reef stretches 2000 km along the Australian coast.

ROTORUA SPRINGS
Hot springs in New Zealand are used to heat nearby homes.

ABORIGINAL PAINTINGS
Aborigines have a tradition of painting on rocks and cave walls.

SYDNEY OPERA HOUSE
The famous shell-shaped roofs were designed to look like giant sails.

MAORI MEETING HOUSE
The Maoris of New Zealand are expert wood carvers.

WAITOMO CAVE
Thousands of glow-worms light up this amazing New Zealand cave.

Design: First Edition
Art Director: Clare Sleven
Project Manager: Susanne Bull
Production Assistant: Ian Paulyn
Artists: Mark Bergin, Roger Smith, Roger Stewart

This is a Parragon Book
This edition published in 2000
Parragon, Queen Street House, 4 Queen Street, Bath, BA1 1HE

2 4 6 8 10 9 7 5 3 1

Produced by Miles Kelly Publishing Ltd,
Bardfield Centre, Great Bardfield, Essex, CM7 4SL

British Library Cataloguing-in-Publication Data
A catalogue record for this book is available from the British Library

ISBN 0 75253 275 8

Printed in Italy
by STIGE Turin